The Video Game

by Brenda Stein Dzaldov and
Cheryl Urback
Photographs by Dave Starrett

The green stars

are falling.

Beep! Beep! Beep!

I have the most stars.

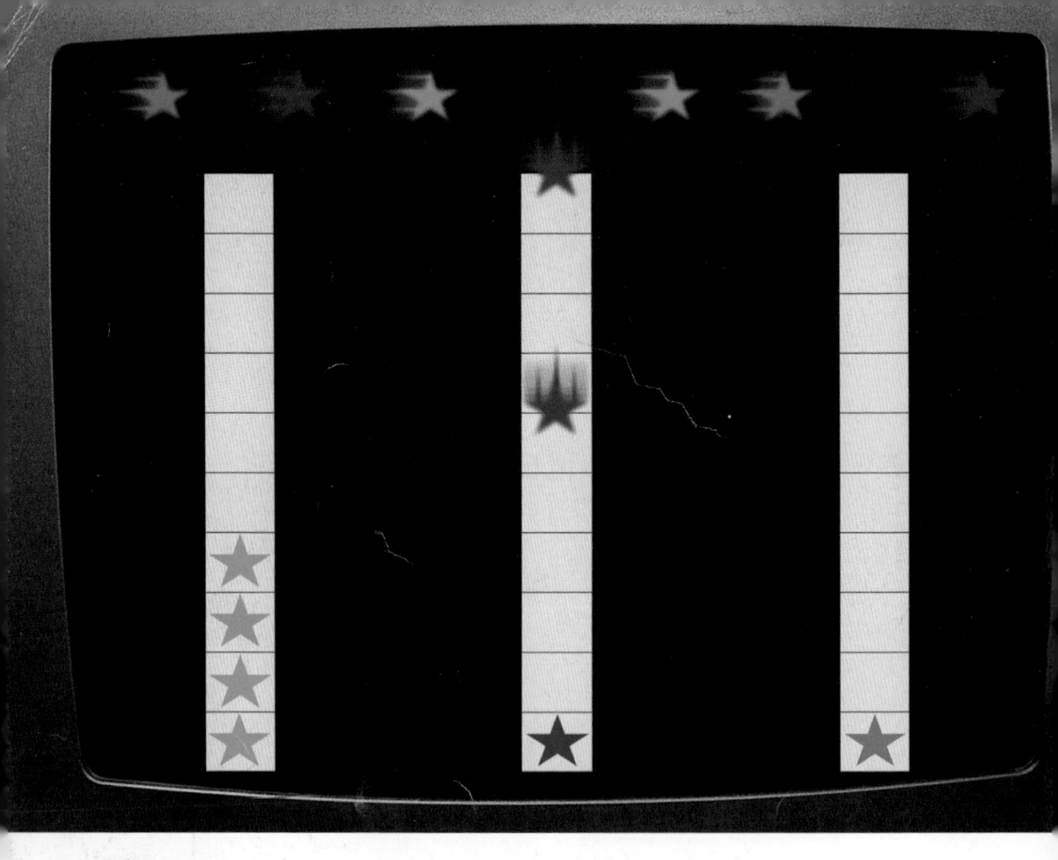

The red stars

are falling.

Beep! Beep!

I have the most stars.

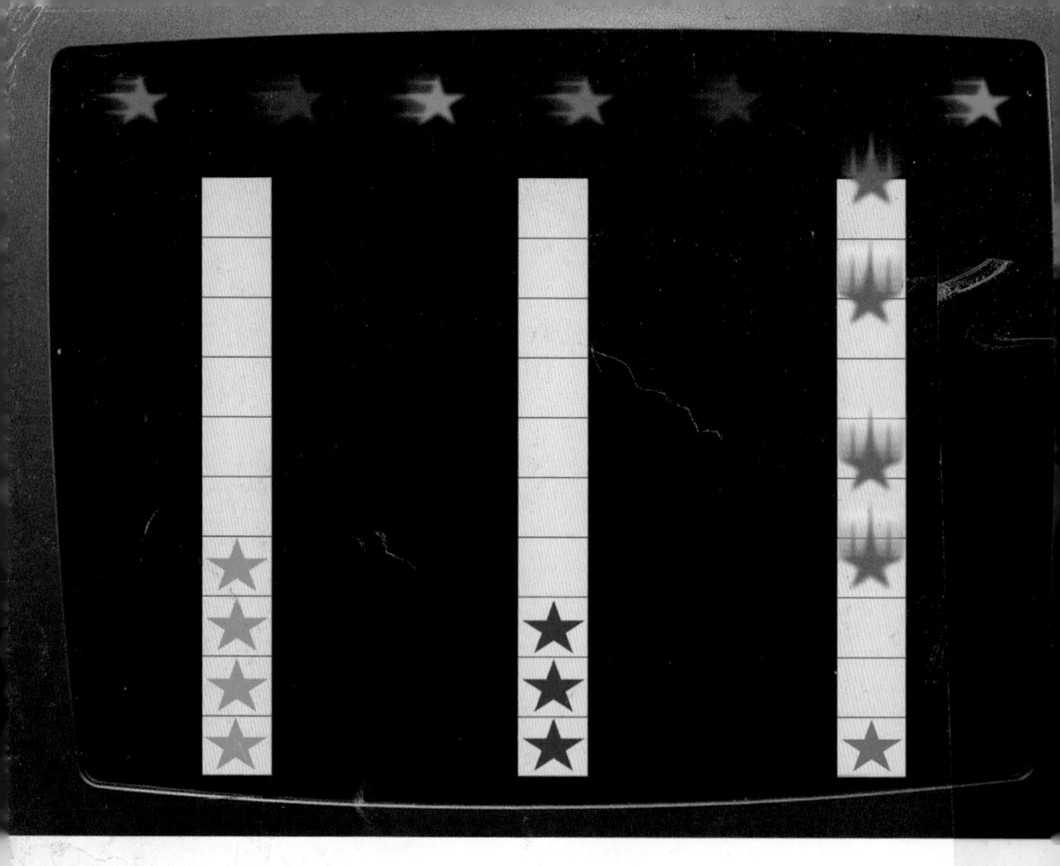

The blue stars

are falling.

Beep! Beep! Beep! Beep!

I have the most stars.

The green stars

are falling.

Beep! Beep! Beep!

I have the most stars.

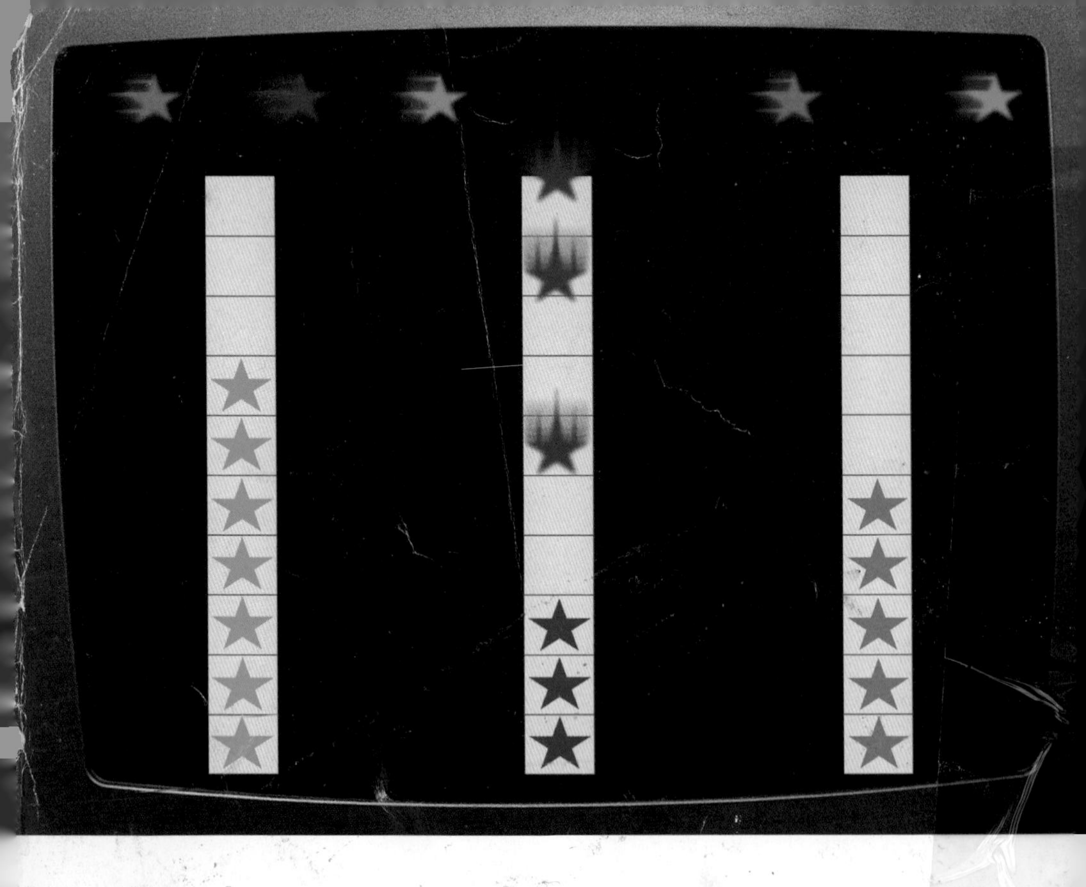

The red stars

are falling

Beep! Beep! Beep!

I have the most stars.

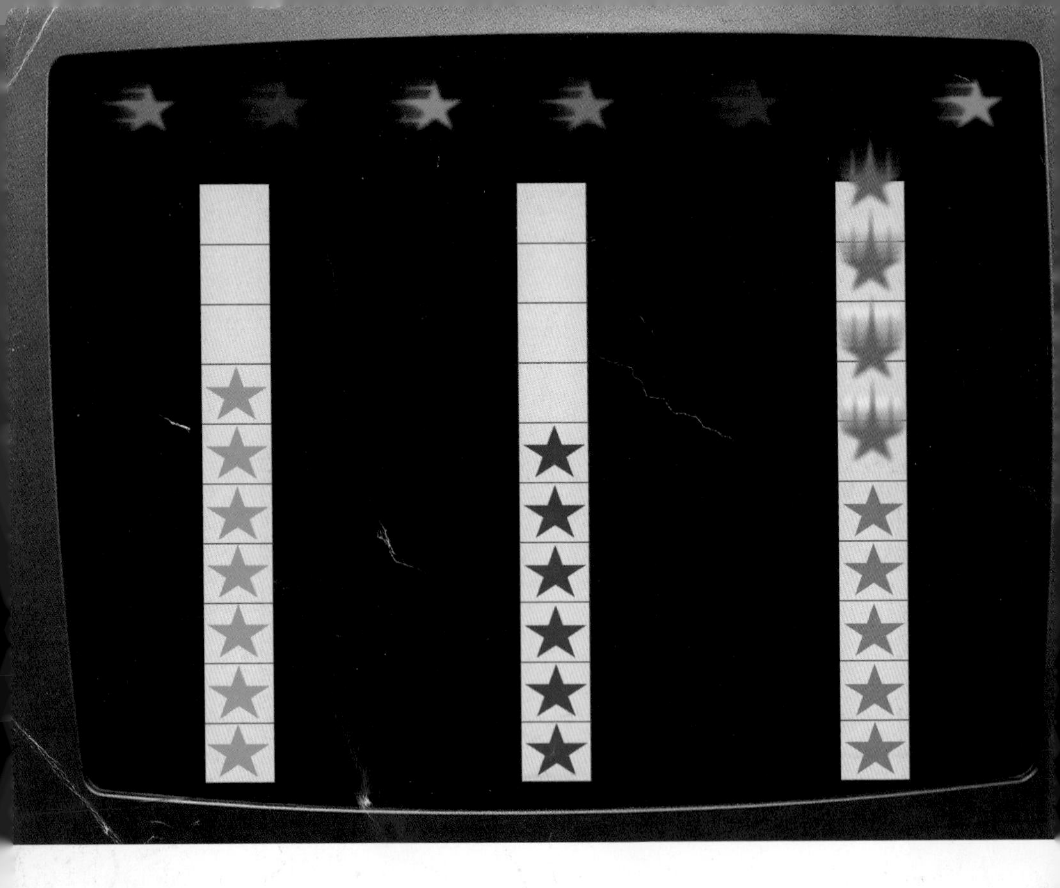

The blue stars

are falling.

Beep! Beep! Beep! Beep!

I have the most stars.

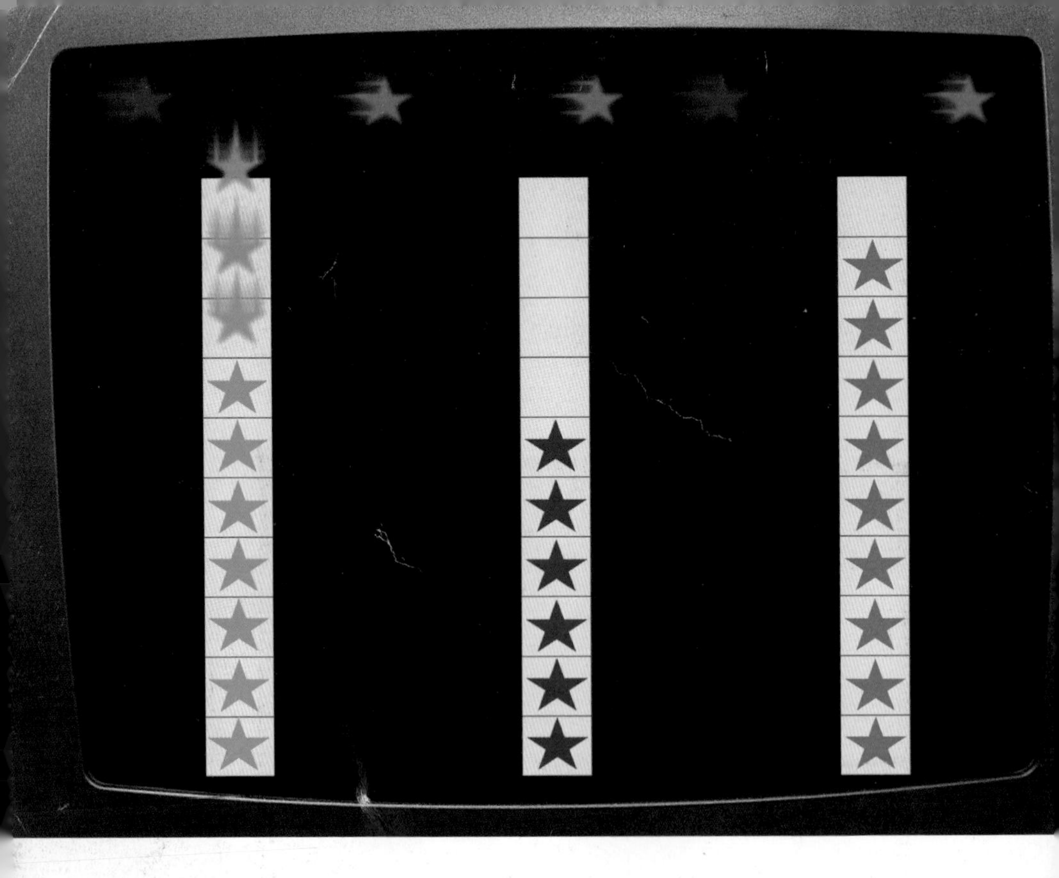

The green stars

are falling.

Beep! Beep! Beep!

I have the most stars.

I win!